Break Your Invisible Chains

Own The Power Of Your Story

An Active Guided Reflection Journal

Brandon Telg, Dr. Jaron Jones, & Carly Barnes

Published by Self Narrate.

Library of Congress Cataloging-In-Publication Data
Break your invisible chains / Brandon Telg, Dr. Jaron Jones, & Carly Barnes — 1st ed.
ISBN: 978-0-9973354-0-8
eISBN: 978-0-9973354-1-5
WC: 10,816

Cover design by Brad Gantt

Publisher info:
Website: www.selfnarrate.com
Email: info@selfnarrate.com
Twitter: @selfnarrate

ACKNOWLEDGEMENTS

It has been a long road getting this book finally written. We want to thank our parents, Tarielle, Lindsey, Elise, and Cam for always being there and supporting us. To Billy and Alise for lending their talents to the cause of storytelling. To Dr. Telg for editing this book. To Jenny for her editing help. To the wonderful storytellers at the UCG class that we taught that became the outline for this book. Finally, to Tony, who was the first to ask us for our story.

This book is dedicated to you, because your story matters.

Break Your Invisible Chains

FORWARD

Stories are in every area of our lives. Each day we add stories to the countless amount that fill our memory banks until resurfacing at the perfect moment to engage those around us. They help us form connections and engage in the world around us. This book is about personal narratives. Narratives go well beyond the traditional anecdotes of what someone did earlier in the day and reveal something much more powerful. They reflect the gripping tales that move us to tears and double us over in laugher. They emerge through intentional reflection versus simple whimsical banter, and provides us insight into the depths of who we are as friends, brothers, sisters, sons, daughters, colleagues, and more. Further, they create an interconnected web of social understanding, and they form the foundation for the relationships that can bring us the most joy while simultaneously bringing the most pain. They bring us to a place of self-awareness and create meaning for our lives. Narratives weave a tapestry that gives meaning to our relationships, creates depth for our communication, and lights our passionate desires through a lexicon of emotions. Simply put – they define us.

In 2013, I found myself teaching a graduate level interpersonal leadership course at the University of Florida. Twelve brave students found themselves in front of me in a weathered conference room that contained dusty once-read dissertations, wobbly chairs, and a failing HVAC systems that made the temperature in the room each day an adventure. The course was grounded in the process of narrative that I had learned while working with an exuberant fun-filled Springsteen lover from New Jersey who happened to find himself, after many twists and turns in the pine-lined streets of Spokane, Washington, in the Pacific Northwest. His name was Joe and the first time I met him he told a story that changed my world from teaching and learning to cultivation and enlightenment. The story seemed simple enough, as he provided a comical tale of his first triathlon and the trials and tribulations that ensued that day. However, at the conclusion of his story, he masterfully weaved it into his narrative. His narrative went deeper. It was not just a story about the first time he was recognized as having value, it was his personal narrative. It defined who he was and illustrated why he served his wife, students, and friends compassionately and altruistically – because they too had value. His narrative connected with me that day. Not only did it evoke emotion, but it transformed the way I worked with students and created deeper meaning for my life. It had become a small piece of who I was and had further defined me.

With my class of twelve, I wanted them to have a similar experience. I wanted them to be transformed. However, I realized that my transformation was not about Joe. Joe definitely played a catalytic role in my transformation, but I had to willingly engage in the transformational process. In an effort to create an environment that would form the foundation for my twelve to transform, I leveraged subtle cues establishing comfort, I removed the wildly oppressive grading systems that most of our higher education institutions are built upon, I gave them permission to fail, and most importantly, I told my narrative. Modeling the behavioral shift that I wanted them to embody led to questions, concerns, and even heartaches as they wrestled with the ambiguity in front of them. However, they persisted and continued to define their narratives.

As the end of the semester neared, the students were faced with a project that asked them to form groups and engage with a community that is different than their own. I asked them to leave the comfort of our weathered conference room, step outside of the building, and do the unthinkable – interact with strangers, thereby pushing their comfort zones and illuminating new opportunities for self-reflection and growth. Three of the students in my class, Jaron, Brandon (your authors into this journey of narrative), and another, decided that they would make a sign on white poster board simply reading, "tell me your story and I will give you a dollar". They headed out to busy areas of campus and the city where they would be approached and told stories. However, what they learned that day, as described weeks later in our conference room, was something much more than a few stories. They found something rich. Something that burned deep inside them that led Jaron to the TED stage and Brandon to shift his career trajectory – they found their passion. Through the stories that homeless people, college students, the mentally ill, professors, business women, and countless other told, they began to define their own narrative. This moment not only led to a deeper sense of self for Jaron and Brandon, it led to the development of Self Narrate – an amazing group that gives voice and value to the world through the process of narrative.

Jaron and Brandon are curious. They love to explore the world through the narratives that we all have and the stories that we all tell. Rob McKee famously wrote that stories are the creative conversion of life itself into something more meaningful. Through the process of narrative, we can allow curiosity to drive our exploration of others and form the foundation for a profound understanding of ourselves.

Jaron and Brandon are authentic. One of the most admirable qualities, which transcends cultural divides and repairs the broken, is authenticity. As I have traveled the globe and worked with populations from Cleveland to Campiñas, from Zambezi to Zurich, and everywhere in between, I have learned that authenticity is the foundation for empathy and empathy is what converts a connection into community. You can see it in their smile and you can feel it in their words. Jaron and Brandon have it and through the process of narrative we can develop it too.

Jaron and Brandon are my friends. When I met them, they were very different people. I have watched them traverse adversity, achieve goals, and grow not only as people but as masterful storytellers who empower change in our world. This book is about their narratives, as only they can tell them, but it has the potential to assist you in defining who you are. For that, I thank them and I wish you all the best in your journey through narrative.

Dr. Anthony Andenoro

PREFACE

What is your story?

You might be thinking to yourself, "Oh, I don't have a story." Or "My story isn't worth telling." Or even, "My story doesn't matter." But the simple truth is this: **You do have a story. And your story matters.**

We all carry an innate desire to discover the meaning of our lives, to connect the dots, to interact with the world, and determine what our experiences mean to us. This quest for self-understanding is part of what makes us human. Humans have been telling stories for as long as we've existed, in order to understand and share the meaning of our experiences.

You are the only person who has lived through your unique experiences in life, who has encountered the same relationships and lessons and hardships at the same moments. No one else ever has or will interact with the world in the exact same way as you. The context of your life generates a wonderfully remarkable setting for your story, and your story alone.

We want to help you identify the key moments in your life, and help you find and share the meaning in those experiences. We want to help you find the truths in your story – about you, your life, and your experiences. Whether or not you realize it yet, each moment of your life has tremendous meaning. Sometimes we just have to look at the big picture in order to discover our stories.

– Brandon Telg, Jaron Jones, Carly Barnes

The Self Narrate Team

CHAPTER ONE: BABY ELEPHANT SYNDROME

Whether you've been to a circus with loved ones or seen a circus act on TV, I'm sure you remember seeing beautiful gigantic elephants performing tricks for the crowd. Children are laughing and families are enjoying themselves, but did you ever stop to think why these enormous animals stay within the confines of the circus tent? Elephants are built to uproot trees using only their trunk, yet these circus elephants never try to leave. Elephants in their natural habitat would break free from their bondage and roam as they pleased. So why don't these circus elephant simply walk out of the circus? It's not like anyone would be able to stop them easily. The reason why circus elephants don't escape is that they believe in false limitations. They believe in invisible chains.

This belief of bondage begins when these huge elephants are babies, barely able to walk on their own. Each circus hires elephant trainers that take these baby elephants and systematically force them to believe that can never escape. To accomplish this, trainers will first take a baby elephant, when it is most vulnerable, out of captivity and into the circus environment. The trainer then takes a huge metal clasp and tightly closes it around the baby elephant's ankle. That ankle clasp is then affixed to a heavy metal chain, which is hammered into the ground using a thick metal stake. It is at that very moment that the baby elephant's instincts kick in. It tells itself that something is terribly wrong and it must break free. The baby elephant notices that it is attached to this contraption and tugs at the chain, panicking as it realizes it cannot escape. An instantaneous tantrum occurs because the baby elephant knows that this bondage is not normal. The baby elephant tries to run. But it can't. It gets snapped back by the chain. The elephant tries to escape again. It can't. The baby elephant knows it's not supposed to be chained down and that it is built to roam the lands. The baby elephant knows that the circumference of a circus tent is not where its story ends. So for two weeks, this baby elephant fights with all of its will, with all of its might, to escape from this chain, because it knows its truth.

After two weeks, this baby elephant becomes tired, frustrated, and defeated. Its will has been broken. With a bloodied ankle, this baby elephant now feels it can never move beyond the distance of this metal clasp and chain. This baby elephant is stuck.

Fast-forward 10 years: this baby elephant has grown to weigh over 6,000 pounds. Even though it is a massive and majestic animal, the circus elephant forever believes it is trapped within the circus tent. Now the trainers only need to tie a small woven rope around its ankle, just tight enough for the elephant to feel its pressure. When the fully grown elephant senses this rope, it believes it is still that same baby elephant. It doesn't know that it can break free. The elephant is bound by invisible chains.

This story shows how in life, the stories people have imposed on us can bind us in invisible chains. We've all had experiences in our lives that have put a clasp on how we define ourselves. When someone else tells you that you can't do something and you believe them, they write your story for you. Believing someone else's story about you influences the actions that you take and where you see your goals in the future. What we have to do is learn about ourselves and become more self aware, more self observant, to identify these invisible chains so we can break free and live our best life!

The goal of this guided reflection journal is to help you break those invisible chains!

PROMPT: What do your invisible chains look like? What are some limitations in your life that someone else has set for you or that you may have set for yourself?

_____

_____

_____

_____

_____

_____

_____

_____

PROMPT: Who trained you? Where did your chains come from? (What have the people you trust in your life told you about yourself that may have given you limitations?)

_____

_____

_____

_____

_____

_____

_____

_____

Invisible chains are tricky because since we can't see them, they can echo in our mind even after the person or group that imposed those chains on us no longer plays an important role in our lives. For example, the parent who tells their child that the child has no chance at being a singer because he or she does not have a superstar "look," can create a mindset of failure in their child. He or she might think that they cannot succeed in their musical ambitions all the way into adulthood and beyond. Invisible chains can be broken, but you have to acknowledge that they are there, where they came from and that they aren't a valid reflection of who you truly are. Invisible chains can lead you into living what is not your most authentic life. Invisible chains can run deep. They can affect how you think about yourself, what relationships you forge, the decisions you make, and risks you take. What kind of reality do you build for yourself based on insecurities that someone else has shoved on you? Typically that reality is a limited one. The mindset might be that for some reason if you apply for that job, or if you move, or if you tell your dad how you really feel, or if you're in a friendship that's toxic for you, you have to re-experience that over and over again through your life. That's really what the invisible chain is. You're re-experiencing being chained to something, believing that's as far as you can go, and you apply that to other situations in your life instead of realizing that you have the freedom to overcome and create a new pattern of positivity and self-growth. This is your circus ring. You <u>can</u> break your invisible chains to live your most authentic life.

To begin to break these invisible chains, this person whose dream it was to be a singer might begin to take vocal lessons or audition for a local singing group. There are many ways to break invisible chains, and often it comes with an action. For some, it's ending a relationship, for others it's apologizing, and for others still, it is starting a new job. The resources are there to break your invisible chains and take a positive step forward, but you must pursue them.

PROMPT: What resources do you need to break your invisible chains?

_____

_____

_____

_____

_____

_____

_____

_____

You must learn from the mistakes

PROMPT: What are some tangible steps that you can begin to take to break those invisible chains?

_____

_____

_____

_____

_____

_____

_____

_____

Through _Breaking Your Invisible Chains_, you will be self-reflecting and analyzing your experiences as a story. You will be looking at your experiences to see what you have overcome and you will create a positive path into your future. You will express what you deep-down already know about yourself but have not yet put on paper. By writing your story through the prompts and questions in this book, you will empower yourself through your own story. You will break your invisible chains.

CHAPTER TWO: INTRODUCTION OF STORY AS A SELF-REFLECTION TOOL

You can break your invisible chains. To be able to do this, you first need to know what these chains are and how they got there. To learn about yourself, you must engage in self-reflection. Self-reflection is deep thought about yourself, your past and your experiences. Different people self-reflect in different ways, but among the most effective methods of self-reflection is personal story development. When you look at your own life experiences and tell them as a story, you are processing your memories in an efficient and beneficial way. Humanity has used storytelling as a way to express experiences since the beginning of mankind, and stories are still how we most effectively share information with each other. Through the course of this guided reflection journal, you will not just be writing a story, but will also dig into your own experiences to be able to express something deep about yourself and your life. After writing your story, you will be equipped with the tools to break your invisible chains.

THE RESEARCH
BY JARON JONES

Developing and sharing your story has a deep impact and a huge benefit. For my dissertation research, I examined how narrative approaches can enhance your self-efficacy and personal hardiness. Self-efficacy is your personal belief in your ability to create a positive change through stressful circumstances and situations. Personal hardiness is your ability to turn stressful situations into opportunities for personal growth. I studied students at the University of Florida in the leadership development program. I helped students develop their story, share it, and after, gauge their understanding of their ability to overcome stressful situations. On all levels of personal hardiness and self-efficacy, I found that there was an increase in each student's belief in their ability to create a positive change through stressful situations. By developing and understanding our stories, we get to turn perceived "weaknesses" into assets. I use quotations around "weaknesses" because when you come to understand your experiences differently, you see how when you've gone through a difficult time, one that could've felt crippling at the time, you are able to re-evaluate it when you develop your story. The mindset usually shifts through thoughts like, "Wow, I went through that? And I'm still here today? Clearly, I'm a very strong person who can do anything."

My research also showed and discussed how each student, in their story, could've taken two different approaches. They could've said, "Oh man, the situation that happened to me really had a negative effect on my life," or "I could turn that negative experience into a positive." Relatedly, when you develop your story, you get to assign meaning to life events, which is empowering! It helps you to understand what you've already been strong enough to overcome and shows that you can overcome anything in the future. The extremely influential German philosopher Friedrich Nietzsche said, "He or she who has a why to live for can bear with almost any how." When you understand your goals, or why you're doing what it is that you're doing in life, there's nothing you can't overcome to achieve those goals.

Finally, what I really love, is that when you share your story, you get to help others. In sharing your story, people are able to pull from your experiences and see life from your perspective. They can relate and see that they've had these same ideas, fears, hopes and dreams. It helps people realize they are not alone in their experiences. The author and public speaker Iyanla Vanzant says that, "When you stand and share your story in an empowering way, your story will heal you and your story will heal somebody else." Storytelling is a community development process, where we all learn and grow from each other's stories.

Meaning-making is the ability to connect one's experiences with meanings to describe the overall self. It has been studied and shown that people who are able to engage in meaning-making, tend to be psychologically healthy and generally happier and more willing to engage with, and try new things.

Your life story changes and adapts to the situations that

arise in your life, and so the meanings that you associate with your memories need to accurately change to reflect your changing experiences.

What memories, then, do you tie meanings to? There are many mundane memories in every person's life, so do we include doing the dishes and taking out the trash in our personal stories? No. The memories that are important are called *self-defining memories*.

Self-reflecting and evaluating our lives can be a tricky task. When one begins to actually sit and think about their story, they can often have a hard time knowing where to begin. It's easy to say to yourself, "There's just too many places to start. Do I begin in childhood and work my way forward? Do I start with where I am now and work my way back?" Clearly, there are many ways to go about this, but we find that it is often easiest to start with the question, "What was the moment when everything changed for me? There was a pre-me and a post-me after that event." You might already begin to see that this is likely your primary self-defining memory. We are able to recall these memories with a good degree of accuracy with little effort. Likely, having just read the question, a moment or two has already materialized in your mind. These moments are of such importance that they change the way that we view ourselves, others, or the situation that we are in. These are the moments that make us who we are. These are the moments that our story is crafted on. When you have that particularly important self-defining memory as an anchor, the rest of your story will likely fall into place.

These moments can be times of great difficulty or wonderful opportunity. The birth of your first child, the failure of a relationship, the completion of college, all of these can be this pivotal moment for you. Let's say that graduating from college is your pivotal moment. What particular challenges did you face in your attempt to graduate? What did you learn through your time in college? What initiated your desire to go to college? How has receiving a degree affected your ability to achieve your goals? How have you grown through college? Starting at these pivotal moments, you are able to ask yourself questions about who you were before and who you have become since. This helps you flesh out your story with what details are truly self-defining memories.

PROMPT: What are your self-defining memories?

_____

_____

_____

_____

_____

_____

_____

_____

_____

_____

_____

_____

_____

_____

_____

_____

_____

_____

_____

_____

_____

_____

PROMPT: How did things change in your life around these memories?

_____

_____

_____

_____

_____

_____

_____

_____

_____

_____

_____

_____

_____

_____

_____

_____

_____

_____

_____

_____

PROMPT: Why are these moments so important in your life?

_____

_____

_____

_____

_____

_____

_____

_____

_____

_____

_____

_____

_____

_____

_____

_____

_____

_____

_____

_____

A story is more than just a few jumbled-together words. There's a structure in every story that you've ever heard.

What is a story? A **story**, at its basic level, is told as a series of connected events that are either written or spoken. When you look at your life as a story, those connected events are the important moments in your life.

Every story can be broken down into three elements, no matter what story it is: **1. a character, 2. a conflict,** and **3. a goal**. Let's take a look at *The Lord of the Rings*, for example. This is a long series of books and movies, but you can really break the entire story down to three elements: the **character**, Frodo. The **goal**, getting his ring into the fires of Mount Doom. Every event from the time Frodo gets the ring to when he throws the ring into the fire are the **conflicts** he overcomes along the way. When you think about your own story: **you** are the **character**, what you want in life are your **goals,** and every obstacle you've overcome, striving to reach those goals are your **conflicts**. Even if you haven't formulated your experiences as a story ever before, it is pretty easy for you to do so with this basic structure. If you identify what a goal is or has been in your life, from there, you can easily identify the conflicts that went into making that goal happen.

If you have never written a story before, it may seem like a difficult task. To show how easy it is to think in terms of character/conflict/goal, we are going to give you three elements right here: A stick-figure human, a brick wall, and a pizza. So we have a character, we have a conflict, and we have a goal. Using these three elements, write a story:

_____

_____

_____

_____

_____

_____

_____

_____

_____

_____

_____

_____

_____

_____

_____

_____

_____

_____

_____

_____

_____

_____

_____

_____

_____

_____

We asked dozens of people to come up with a story on the spot using these three elements. We were told fantasy stories, stories about the stick figure digging a hole, walking around the wall, scaling the wall, and everything in between. Every time, we still see a defined character, conflict, and goal. No two stories look alike, and that's amazing! It is likely that what you wrote involves the person attempting to get the pizza. That is a story with a character overcoming a conflict to reach his goal. When you take these story elements and apply them to your life as you self-reflect, you will be surprised how your story structures itself.

Why create your story?

Through creating your story, you develop emotional awareness, self-reflection, and personal growth. You discover how events in your life have impacted you, then you decide how those impacts will continue to affect you. What happened that challenged your path to success or happiness? How did you handle it? What lessons have you learned? Are you still learning? Questions like these help shape your understanding of your past and empower you to engage in your future. The key is that your values can inspire action through emotion. Learning to identify your values will help you bring about positive life changes. In deciding how to move forward, you are able to break your invisible chains and forge a new path.

Through this journal you will break your invisible chains through the processes of:

Developing

To understand your life in a deeper, more meaningful way, first you need to understand it as a story. Have you ever thought of your life as a story? Creating your story helps you to understand your motivations, passions, and purpose.

Externalizing

Once you have created your story, growth comes from sharing it. Whether with one person or a group, a deeper level of understanding comes from the sharing of stories.

Internalizing

Use this greater understanding of your self to live the story that you want to share.

As you begin to craft your story, you want to answer three questions. (Don't worry, we'll get there in the next few chapters.):

1. Who is the lead character? (Since you are the lead character, we'll be defining who you are.)

2. What is my goal? (What do I, the lead character, want?)

3. What conflicts or barriers did I overcome to achieve that goal?

PROMPT: Are you where you want to be right now? Why or why not?

_____
_____
_____
_____
_____
_____
_____
_____
_____
_____
_____
_____
_____
_____
_____

CHAPTER THREE: CHARACTER

The concept of **character** in a story is both simple and complex. Simple characters are merely people in a story that do something. Interesting characters, however, are those that we can relate to and want to see succeed in their mission. We need to understand who they are, what they care about, what their values are. These elements show an audience who the character really is.

In your story, you are the main character. Writers often have a difficult time defining the main character in their works because they have to start from scratch with their characters' defining attributes. You have an advantage because you know what your interests are and what you value. To be able to break your invisible chains, you must first understand who you are and how you got to where you are today. Let's get these attributes on paper.

PROMPT: What are ten words that describe who you are?

_____	_____
_____	_____
_____	_____
_____	_____
_____	_____

PROMPT: What is most important to you? Why?

_____

_____

_____

_____

_____

_____

_____

_____

_____

_____

_____

_____

_____

_____

PROMPT: How would you like to be remembered? What would you want said about you at your funeral?

_____

_____

_____

_____

_____

_____

_____

_____

_____

_____

_____

_____

_____

_____

_____

_____

_____

_____

_____

_____

PROMPT: What were some moments of great change in your life?

_____

_____

_____

_____

_____

_____

_____

_____

_____

_____

_____

_____

_____

_____

_____

_____

_____

_____

_____

_____

_____

PROMPT: Did these moments have an effect on what was most important in your life?

_____

_____

_____

_____

_____

_____

_____

_____

_____

_____

_____

_____

_____

_____

_____

_____

_____

_____

_____

_____

_____

PROMPT: Define the most important people to you in your life. Describe them.

_____

_____

_____

_____

_____

_____

_____

_____

_____

_____

_____

_____

_____

_____

_____

_____

_____

_____

_____

_____

PROMPT: If money was no object and you could do one thing for the rest of your life, what would it be?

PROMPT: What are your hobbies? What do you like to do with your time?

_____

_____

_____

_____

_____

_____

_____

_____

_____

_____

JARON'S STORY

For as long as I can remember, I have wanted to be a leader in my community. I was raised by an amazing family that taught me the best gift in the world was to create a better place for those around you. My mother would preach to me how we were created to do great things, and it's every person's duty to live their best life. I also recall assisting my grandfather with his campaign as city alderman, which he won multiple terms. He taught me by example the importance of serving those within your community. These memories drove me to pursue positions of leadership. I wanted to assist people by helping to create a better tomorrow, and I found joy in working within groups to achieve these goals.

Though I grew up rich in love and support, we really didn't have much money. My mother worked day and night to provide for us and even with the long hours, there were times we came home to no lights. Those were the moments that ignited a fire within me. Tears would fall down my cheeks when I would see the frustration and stress not having enough money would cause my mother. She worked harder than anyone I knew, and I always wanted her to be paid what she deserved. Understanding this, I wanted to grow up as quickly as possible and make a ton of money so that she would never have to work again. Since I wasn't old enough to work a real job, I became a baby entrepreneur. I had a snow cone business when I was 10, I sold boxes of candy throughout middle school and I worked several fast food and retail jobs while in high school. I even had a hand-painted T-shirt business that I ran out of my bedroom. I slowly began to define my success solely upon my ability to make money by holding a job that paid well.

I went to college, got a full scholarship in a major that desperately needed people to work in that field, and upon graduation, started working for the federal government as a soil scientist. Throughout this entire process my mother would always ask if I was truly happy. I never understood why she kept asking me this because, according to my bank account as a recently graduated 22-year-old with no student loans, I was supposed to be the happiest guy on earth. But that was far from the truth and my mother could see what I couldn't. She told me she missed seeing me perform on stage, speaking to organizations, interacting with my community, making beautiful music, and being the creative young man that she raised. Yes, the bills were getting paid, but my soul was unfulfilled because I was not walking in my truth.

Through self-reflecting upon my past and my life experiences, I remembered that my true passion and purpose was in teaching others to lead according to their passions and life story. I was put on this earth to teach others their truth: to be authentic leaders. To do this effectively, I had to first be very honest with myself and make changes in certain areas that were distancing me from my truth. All the money in the world couldn't add up to the amazing feeling that I felt when I remembered my "why" and started living my best life again.

PROMPT: What elements of Jaron's character do you see in this story?

PROMPT: What does Jaron value? What is important to him?

_____

_____

_____

_____

_____

_____

_____

_____

PROMPT: How did he show these elements of his character?

_____

_____

_____

_____

_____

_____

_____

_____

_____

Jaron's story demonstrates how to use one's experiences to define a story's "character." Jaron describes in detail the experiences that shaped him. We come to understand his family and his community life from the details he included. He describes how his passion for helping others came from seeing examples of altruism within his family. This passion carried throughout his life and the examples from childhood helped us to understand why it is such a fundamental element of his character. He also describes what caused him to live with invisible chains, living in a situation where there just wasn't enough money. Not being able to control that situation while he was young, he allowed himself to believe that the pursuit of money was more important than following his truth. As you can see in Jaron's story, it is impossible to live your best life while living with an invisible chain. Once he identified his invisible chain, he was able to break it and write a new story for his life. You can also see in Jaron's story that by providing details about who you are and where your motivations came from in life, you can craft a compelling character out of your own experiences.

We come to understand characters best when we see how they fare under pressure. A character's choices show us who they are. Facing moments of great difficulty, and acting in a way consistent with their defined values, shows us a character's strength. In your own story, understanding that you have been strong in moments of difficulty also shows you that you are a strong person who can break your invisible chains.

PROMPT: Is there one story or experience from your life that you think defines you as a character?

_____

_____

_____

_____

_____

_____

_____

_____

_____

_____

_____

_____

_____

_____

_____

PROMPT: What are some moments where you showed your strength?

_____

_____

_____

_____

_____

_____

_____

_____

_____

_____

_____

_____

_____

_____

_____

_____

_____

_____

_____

_____

_____

CHAPTER FOUR: CONFLICT

In life, everyone goes through conflict. Whether this conflict is a small disagreement or a long-term struggle, it can all feel equally painful to go through while it is happening.

For many, reminders of conflict can put them right back in the state of mind that they were in while the conflict was happening. When you take a step back and look at your life as a story, you get to see conflicts from a mile-high view which creates distance from these emotionally charged experiences. Rather than looking at them as personal tragedies or hardships, look at your conflicts as obstacles that you overcame in your journey.

PROMPT: Write out some past conflicts in your life.

_____

_____

_____

_____

_____

_____

_____

_____

_____

_____

PROMPT: How did you overcome these conflicts?

_____

_____

_____

_____

_____

_____

_____

_____

_____

_____

PROMPT: If you could go back and talk to yourself while you were going through these conflicts, what would you tell yourself?

_____

_____

_____

_____

_____

_____

_____

_____

_____

_____

BRANDON'S STORY

For as long as I can remember, I wanted to work in theater. I wasn't interested in performing, but in making the performances possible. I studied stage management in college, and was fortunate to be hired into my dream job right after graduation. As a newly minted University of Central Florida alumnus, I began working for Cirque du Soleil as a stage manager for their Orlando show, La Nouba. This show is a breathtaking production and I felt so blessed to get to watch and work with this show from the ground floor. However, I experienced my very own plot twist-worthy conflict when I unexpectedly became a father at the young age of 21.

I continued to work at Cirque du Soleil after my daughter was born. This was unexpectedly challenging because working in the theater typically requires you to be away from home in the evenings. So here I was, getting home from work very late into the night each night, then not getting any sleep at home because as soon as I would lay down in bed I would be awoken by my baby's cries. If only I would have been able to sleep in during the morning but the baby's internal clock did not care for my lack of rest. I was stressed from sleep deprivation, but motivated from the perception that I had everything I could ask for in my life. The days were hard and tiring, but I had faith that when my daughter grew older, things would balance out.

At work, my colleagues knew that I was a new father. As in any work environment, people want to provide advice to those who are walking a path they've already strode. I received a lot of great new father advice, but over time, this parental banter soured. My coworkers started complaining to me about missing their kids' baseball games, dance recitals and Boy Scout troop meetings. I would hear the stories of these parents who felt very distant from their children because they, too, would get home extremely late at night and need to sleep through the morning, while their kids are getting ready for school, then leave to go to work before the kids got home from school. They rarely got to spend time with their children and regretted it. These conversations happened every night.

Negative thoughts began to seep into my mind, "will I become a distant father by pursuing my passion?" "What kind of relationship will I have with my child in ten years?" I realized that I was faced with a major life conflict. Which do I value more: family or career? Either I could continue to pursue my dream job, or I could have a relationship with my child. This question ate away at me. I had invested my life in the theater. It was my dream. But this child gave me unconditional love in a way that I had never felt and I wanted my relationship with her to grow.

So I made the decision to quit. Not just from this job, but theater in general. It seemed like a difficult decision, but once it was made, I knew it was truly the only choice. I relocated to start a master's program at the University of Florida because I knew that having a relationship with my child was more important to me than any job could possibly be, even theater.

PROMPT: What conflicts did you see in Brandon's story?

PROMPT: How did he overcome these conflicts?

_____

_____

_____

_____

_____

_____

_____

_____

_____

_____

_____

PROMPT: What would you have told Brandon in this situation?

_____

_____

_____

_____

_____

_____

_____

_____

_____

_____

_____

Brandon's story shows us that conflict is always present throughout life and it is vital that we constantly reevaluate what's most important to us. His will to provide for his daughter gave him the strength to overcome the stressors of sleep deprived nights to do what needed to be done at work. As his story continues, you see him battle internally with whether or not he should continue a life of theater or find a new normal that would support his wanting to be a good father for his daughter. We see the conflicts change within his life, but we also see that one story remains the same; no matter what, Brandon wants to be a good father to his daughter. Through reflecting on how he overcame his past conflicts, Brandon reaffirms that being a good father is what's most important to him and his decision to start a new life outside of theater was the best decision for his family.

While conflicts are difficult, they should not be avoided in your story. They are what makes people sit up and pay attention. Every story has a main character and an ending, but good stories have many conflicts. A story's conflicts are when we get to see what the character is made of. We get to see them grow and break the chains that hold them back from their goal.

If we don't properly process our past conflicts, they can end up shackling us to negative mindsets. Conflict not properly analyzed in your story can become that small rope tied to the elephant's foot, keeping you tied down when you really have the strength to be your free and true self. Conflicts are the things that you've overcome, the things that you were strong enough to get through. When you see your conflicts for what they are, you realize that what may have been perceived as a weakness is actually an asset. You are stronger than your conflicts.

PROMPT: What traits do you see in your self that came as direct results of conflicts that you overcame?

_____

_____

_____

_____

_____

_____

_____

_____

_____

_____

_____

_____

_____

_____

_____

PROMPT: What did you learn about yourself from your conflicts?

_____

_____

_____

_____

_____

_____

_____

_____

_____

PROMPT: In what ways are you a stronger person after overcoming these conflicts?

_____

_____

_____

_____

_____

_____

_____

_____

_____

CHAPTER FIVE: GOAL

Defining a goal and striving for it helps us find meaning in our lives. Viktor Frankl, author of *Man's Search For Meaning*, created a form of psychological analysis called Logotherapy. One of the core concepts in Logotherapy is the belief that the primary motivation of human beings is to find meaning in our own lives. One way we do this is by achieving goals. Clearly defined goals help us to see a purpose for the work we do.

Goals can be lofty or modest. If you haven't made a goal for yourself in a while, start with something small. As the famous theologian C.S. Lewis said, "You are never too old to set another goal or to dream a new dream." Think of something you've wanted to do for a while, like "learn how to bake a pineapple upside-down cake." Write it on a sticky note, and then do it! Come up with another goal, a bigger goal, and then do it! Once you've got momentum, you'll find that goal setting becomes easier and your goals will likely get larger.

PROMPT: What was the last goal that you achieved?

_____

_____

_____

_____

_____

_____

_____

_____

_____

_____

_____

PROMPT: What are your primary goals now?

_____

_____

_____

_____

_____

_____

_____

_____

_____

PROMPT: What inspired you to pursue your goals?

_____

_____

_____

_____

_____

_____

_____

_____

CARLY'S STORY

For as long as I can remember, I've wanted to build my career -- and life -- around changing the world. From living in a hut in the desert somewhere on the other side of the world, to teaching in an inner city -- you name the humanitarian cause or experience, and I was into it. By the time I was 19, I had completed an undergraduate degree and half of my master's program at the University of Florida, studying communication and change within agricultural communities and food systems. (People needed my help, so I was in a hurry.) I accepted a job that would take me from warm and sunny north central Florida to the temperate, cold rainforest of the Alaskan panhandle and to a much different type of island town than I was used to called Sitka. I was stoked. I was going to document land use changes in the Tongass National Rainforest that would contribute to more sustainable forest systems. (How cool is that?!) That is, until I got sick again.

I'll fast forward through the next couple of years:

I started running high fevers every day, getting migraines, having seizures, heart palpitations, and all kinds of weird symptoms. I decided to stay in Florida, working at the university and finishing my master's degree to stay closer to my doctors. I kept getting sicker and sicker, and a year later was walking with a cane and no diagnosis. I ended up quitting my job and school, moved back home where my parents lived, was told that I had chronic fatigue, and would be that sick forever. I then met a guy, we started dating and then we got engaged. I finally got a real diagnosis and started two very hard years of treatment. Those were also two very hard years during my relationship with said guy. I was constantly being told that I had the "potential to be a good person" even though I was a "snob" and "not nice to people." Hearing this, I started to believe it. I believed I was stuck in a town where I wasn't able to make a difference. I believed I was "stuck" in a suffocating environment. I believed that I was "stuck" in an unhealthy relationship because I wasn't worthy of friendship or love. I believed that my dreams were silly and unattainable and naive. I believed that I should stick around and get married because that's what I was supposed to do with my life and because no one else would want to marry me. I believed that my worldview and expectations should be much, much smaller. Then I went on a business trip and came home to find out I wasn't engaged anymore. So I loaded up my dog and what little self esteem I had left and moved back to the town where I went to college.

And then everything came back to me. I reconnected with all of the good things I once wanted to do. Within six weeks, I completed my requirements to actually graduate with my master's degree. I looped back in with my doctors and finally reached a point where I wasn't just surviving, but my health was really thriving. I found my "tribe" of people and found invaluable joy in having meaningful friendships and community. I found ways to connect and use my skill set to volunteer and make a difference. I found my love for music again. I found my love for serving people again. Most importantly, I found my love for my most authentic self again.

And guess what? I plan to begin a doctoral program in the fall, and I began a new job where I get to help people solve one of the world's biggest health challenges. I wake up thankful each day to have the chance to contribute to the world. And now that I'm back in touch with my goals, I have promised myself that with every fiber of my being, I will never let any illness, person, or circumstance steer me away from what resonates with me as my highest calling.

PROMPT: What goals did you see in Carly's story?

_____

_____

_____

_____

_____

_____

_____

_____

_____

_____

PROMPT: How did she pursue her goals?

_____

_____

_____

_____

_____

_____

_____

_____

_____

_____

_____

PROMPT: What happened when she stopped pursuing her goals?

_____

_____

_____

_____

_____

_____

_____

_____

_____

_____

_____

PROMPT: What would you have told Carly in this situation?

_____

_____

_____

_____

_____

_____

_____

_____

_____

PROMPT: How would you describe Carly's outlook now that she is pursuing her goals?

_____

_____

_____

_____

_____

_____

_____

Carly's story is an interesting example of what happens

when you live with goals, and when you live without them. When she was 19, Carly had big goals: she wanted to make a positive impact on the world in regions that typically get overlooked. She wanted to make a difference. When she got sick, she was physically unable to pursue this goal for a time. She operated without an overarching personal goal, due to life circumstances, and in this period, began to believe someone else's story for her life. This caused her to have a very negative worldview. When she reconnected with her personal goals, life became vibrant again. For part of her story, while she was listening to messages of negativity that made her question her self-worth, Carly allowed invisible chains to be placed on her. It wasn't until she reconnected with her personal goals that she broke her invisible chains and is now living a meaningful and joyful life, making a difference for others.

Many people operate without goals in life. We encourage you to always have a goal. Not only is it part of your story, but pursuing goals can give your life a greater sense of meaning. When we talk about the goal that your story is based around, they can be your primary goals in this moment of your life, or these could be the goals that you have had over the course of your life. It's however you want to define that term "goal." For some, a goal can be as simple as getting out of bed in the morning, or it can be as big as visiting every country on the map. Write whatever a goal looks like to you. If you can't identify any premeditated goals, now is a great time to come up with some new ones.

PROMPT: What are some of the ways that you're pursuing your goals?

_____

_____

_____

_____

_____

_____

_____

_____

_____

_____

_____

_____

_____

_____

_____

_____

PROMPT: Have your conflicts changed your ability to achieve your goals?

_____
_____
_____
_____
_____
_____
_____
_____
_____

PROMPT: When it comes to attaining your goals, are you where you want to be right now? Why or why not?

_____
_____
_____
_____
_____
_____
_____
_____
_____

PROMPT: What can you do from this moment forward to achieve your goals and be where you want to be?

_____

_____

_____

_____

_____

_____

_____

_____

_____

_____

_____

_____

_____

_____

_____

_____

_____

_____

_____

_____

_____

CHAPTER SIX: PUTTING IT ALL TOGETHER

We've discussed the idea of character, conflict, and goal as the building blocks of your story, and you've written a lot about each one from your personal experiences. Where do we go from here?

You have an idea of what the character, conflict and goal elements of your story are, so how do you move forward in actually writing your story? The answer is by beginning to order events in your mind *as a story*. The story structure of character, conflict and goal gives you the pieces of the puzzle that you will use when you begin to put things together.

When you think of any story, true or fictional, that you've encountered in your life, it typically follows an arc. It begins with a description of the character as they are at the beginning of the story (personality, description of their life conditions and overall life situation). At some point, a goal is established for the character and the audience comes to understand why the goal is important to the character. Something inspires the character to pursue that goal, and whatever that is, is called the inciting incident, or "call to action." The action of the story has now begun. From here, the character is on their way in the pursuit of their goal, but of course, an obstacle (conflict) prevents them in some way from reaching their goal. The character overcomes that conflict somehow. From here, the character may overcome any number of new and difficult conflicts, until eventually, the character reaches their goal. In many stories, you learn at the end what the status quo looks like post-goal attainment for the character.

You can clearly see how character, conflict, and goal are embedded into a story arc. And of course, include lots of description. The more detail and the richer the account of your experiences, the more compelling the story is. If you sit down and write out these situations for yourself, with you as the main character, you will have your story written. It seems daunting at first, but if you break it down with these steps, your authentic story will flow.

Now that we've briefly run through what it looks like, let's break down the steps, in order, in a "cheat sheet" format for when you're writing your story. We've answered these questions in previous chapters. Using what you've written, go ahead and answer these questions to write your story:

PROMPTS:

1. Define your character using descriptive details. What is your background? What do you value?

2. Describe what your goal is and how you discovered that goal.

3. Describe what made you decide to actually pursue your goal.

4. Now that you're pursuing your goal, what obstacles are in your way, preventing you from achieving that goal?

5. What did you do to overcome those obstacles?

6. If you've achieved your goal, how did you do it? If you haven't achieved it yet, where are you in your journey to reach it?
    a. What does your life look like now that you've accomplished your goal?

7. What does the future hold?

Extra Tip! And, And, But, Therefore

If you've never written your story before, a helpful tool to help you structure it is "**And, And, But, Therefore**." The "**And, And, But, Therefore**" method can be used to enhance any story.

- The use of **And** connects details that paint the picture of your story, the way in which you choose to pursue your goal. Two **And's** are used to encourage you, as the storyteller, to provide your audience with more supporting details about your story.
- The use of **But** shows that you encountered a conflict.
- The use of **Therefore** signifies how you overcame the conflict and what the result was.

You can use as many **And's, But's** or **Therefore's** as your story needs.

_____
_____
_____
_____
_____
_____
_____
_____
_____

_____

_____

_____

_____

_____

_____

_____

_____

_____

_____

_____

_____

_____

_____

_____

_____

_____

_____

_____

_____

_____

_____

_____

_____

_____
_____
_____
_____
_____
_____
_____
_____
_____
_____
_____
_____
_____
_____
_____
_____
_____
_____
_____
_____
_____
_____
_____
_____

CHAPTER SEVEN: SELF EMPATHY

You've written your story. Give it a day. Come back to it and re-read your story.

PROMPT: Do you see evidence of any invisible chains in your story?

_____

_____

_____

_____

_____

_____

_____

_____

_____

_____

_____

PROMPT: Have you broken any of these invisible chains? What would it take to break them, if not?

_____

_____

_____

_____

_____

_____

_____

_____

_____

_____

PROMPT: What would you go back and tell the version of you that is going through this story's conflict?

_____

_____

_____

_____

_____

_____

_____

_____

_____

We can be hard on ourselves when we write our stories. We look at our past sometimes as someone who was just more naive or didn't make decisions that you would have. If that past version of yourself hadn't experienced what they did, you wouldn't be who you are today. You wouldn't have the strength that you now have.

BRANDON:

I have been an avid journaler since I was in high school. Nearly every day I write about what is going on in my life. My stack of old journals is a priceless chronicle of my personal experiences. Thumbing through any of them at random allows myself easy access to memories long forgotten. However, there is a more benefit that these journals provide: access to past mindsets.

I recently read through my journal from the most difficult period of my life, when my life completely fell apart. In the span of two years, I found out that I was going to be a parent, I got married, I quit my dream career, and things went south in my personal life. I drained all of my savings, I got divorced and I ended up living in my parents' house because I had nowhere else to go. This period of time was fraught with turmoil coming from every direction externally, but also within my own mind.

As I read through my journal from this time, I see now that "past Brandon" always thought he was doing the wrong thing. I blamed myself for everything that went wrong. Every day, I beat myself up for not doing enough, for not being able to fix every problem, for not being good enough. I look back at those experiences now and see them for what they are: someone trying to do his best. Everyone in my life was trying to do their best. We all just had insufficient tools to handle what we were experiencing.

At this stage of my life, when I read my former thoughts, I feel a lot of empathy for the young man going through all of that strife. I just want to help him by rewriting his story. I was operating with invisible chains that I could not break because I could not acknowledge them. In my mind, I have undergone the process of rewriting my story of what happened, injecting empathy for myself and everyone involved in these experiences. No longer was I the put upon martyr or the failure who could not work hard enough to fix everything, but now I see myself for someone who genuinely tried, showed a great deal of strength and fortitude in difficult times, and came out of it all a wiser person.

When we look at our stories with some distance in time or personal detachment, we have the ability to glean new insight in the positive elements that exist in our stories. I am grateful of my journals because I feel a greater degree of self-empathy and I have a better sense of how far I've come.

PROMPT: Go back and rewrite your story as if you are editing someone else's story. Give yourself more empathy. Think "this person was doing the best they could" and frame the story as one of affirmation.

_____

_____

_____

_____

_____

_____

_____

_____

_____

_____

_____

_____

_____

_____

_____

_____

_____

_____

_____

_____

_____

_____

_____

_____

CHAPTER EIGHT: SHARING

Stories have the power to heal. If you reflect on the difficult times of your life and understand your experiences as a story, you can be an advocate and help others in their times of trouble. If you have already walked down a difficult road that someone else is going down, share your story. It is powerful to know that someone else out there knows what it feels like in the hard times.

BRANDON:

Recently, I led a story development workshop and a female participant shared a story about when she quit her job after 25 years to pursue a new life path. I was conflicted about some personal decisions I needed to make in my own life about which opportunities I would pursue. Hearing this woman share how she fought with herself but ultimately chose what she knew was right for her, helped me to make the decision I knew I needed to make. Her story healed me in a way that I didn't expect. It gave me the confidence to listen to my heart. Our stories have the power to heal.

The amazing part is that by sharing your story, you heal yourself as well. By sharing your story, you internalize your experiences and reveal to yourself the strength you have. By recounting difficult times, it helps you realize that you can overcome anything because you already have.

BRANDON:

In that same story development workshop, I shared the story I shared with you early of how I was faced with a huge conflict a few years ago: career or family. Which is more important? I was beginning a theatrical career but I also had a newborn daughter. I began to realize the theater lifestyle and that of being a parent were not compatible for me. I chose to give up my theatrical ambitions and focus on my family, figuring out another career path along the way. For years, this was my secret shame. I was happy that I chose a relationship with my daughter over my own ambitions, but I never felt that I could share this with anyone. I felt like I gave up. Like I was a failure. It wasn't until I started sharing these experiences in these workshops as an example of a time that I had to make a hard choice that I actually began to look at the path that I took as an indicator of my strength and resilience. Sharing my story helped me to break my chains of shame and begin to heal.

To be a help to others in difficult times, to be a better advocate, to heal yourself, share your story.

Now that you've written-out your story, the next step is to

share your story with someone. Find someone that you trust to share your story with. Whether this person is a friend or a family member, they need to be someone that you can be vulnerable with because story sharing is a vulnerable process. In fact being vulnerable is the key to story sharing. Set aside some time with them, however long you think it will take to share your story. Provide them with the next page, and then share your story.

INFORMATION FOR STORY LISTENER

Hi there! You are reading this because you've been entrusted to listen to an amazing life story. The person that gave you this is trusting you to hear their story as they share it for the first time! Consider yourself lucky as this is a great privilege! Storytelling is a vulnerable act, so there is only one thing asked of you: you need to create a safe space for the story sharing to happen. If you follow three simple steps, you can create a safe, affirming space for story sharing anywhere.

1. Establish trust

Make sure that the person who is sharing their story with you knows that what they share stays with you. The storyteller is about to get vulnerable, so you owe it to them not to betray that trust.

2. Listen

It sounds simple, but it can be difficult in the moment to stay quiet and just listen. It is a natural human tendency to want to talk people through their issues, adding your opinions and advice. This is really not what people want when they're sharing their stories. If someone wants your advice, they will ask you for it. Wait until they are done sharing their story before you ask any follow-up questions.

3. Stay affirming

After someone finishes sharing their story with you, thank them for sharing their story! Tell them how sharing their story made you feel and how it resonated with you. If you want to know more about a moment that they described in their story, ask them! It shows that you were paying close attention. To really dig deep, ask them these two questions:

- Out of all the stories in your life, why did you pick that one?
- How did it feel to share your story with me?

Now get ready to hear an amazing story!

Prompt: How did it feel to share your story?

_____

_____

_____

_____

_____

_____

_____

_____

_____

_____

_____

_____

_____

_____

_____

_____

_____

_____

_____

_____

_____

_____

_____

Prompt: Did sharing your story out loud change how you felt about any parts of your story?

_____

_____

_____

_____

_____

_____

_____

_____

_____

_____

Prompt: How would you share your story differently next time?

_____

_____

_____

_____

_____

_____

_____

_____

_____

CHAPTER NINE: THE END

When you come to the end of a book or a movie and you see those two words "The End," you know that the story is over. The difference between fiction and reality is that your story never ends. That's the beauty of personal storytelling. You can keep coming back and looking at your story again and again from different perspectives at different points in your life. In two, ten, or even twenty years, your life may look completely different. Your story may be completely different. You have the privilege to go back and self-reflect and identify your story again and again. You will learn more about yourself, gaining deeper insight on your identity, every time you write out your story. Brandon, in Chapter 7, described how this happened for him. He realized that his own conception of his past was an invisible chain and he broke it by rewriting his story in his own mind. Once you see where your invisible chains are, break them. You've written your story. You can see that you are not ruled by someone else's version of your story. Live your story on your terms.

Continue to look at your life as a story, so that you can live your best story every day. Once you've broken your invisible chains, encourage others to do the same. Share your story, and ask others for their stories. As the great poet Maya Angelou said: "There is no agony like bearing an untold story inside of you." We all go through difficult times. In our darkest moments it can feel like there's nobody else out there who understands where we are in our lives. In these times of trouble, hearing the stories of someone else who has been through the same issue and come out the other end can be a powerful experience. It can be that revelation that shows that there is hope. Never forget: Your story matters.

ABOUT THE AUTHORS

Brandon Telg is the co-founder of the storytelling company Self Narrate and is a published expert on personal growth through storytelling. He lives in Gainesville, Florida with his wife, daughter and record collection.

Dr. Jaron Jones is the co-founder of the storytelling company Self Narrate and is a nationally recognized speaker/storyteller. His research specializes in using narrative approaches to enhance self-awareness, self-efficacy, personal hardiness, and diversity within leadership environments. He resides in Gainesville, Florida with his wife, his beat machine, and video equipment.

Carly Barnes is a strategist and expert in communication and change management, She is passionate about helping good people do good things, and lives in Gainesville with her quirky Australian shepherd, Camellia.